D1088712

H

Genius

Vulgar
Imitation

Birds

Words and birds by Robert Jay Lifton

First Printing

9 8 7 6 5 4 3 2

 Published in the United States by Random House, Inc., New York, and simultaneously in Canada by Random House of Canada Limited, Toronto.

Library of Congress Catalog Card Number:
75-89698

Manufactured in the United States of America

To my bird, Beej

Life

All of a sudden I had this wonderful feeling: "I am me!"
You were wrong.

What am I doing here?
That is not a scientific question.

why are you so lascivious?
Dionysus is using me.

If you were a baby waiting up in heaven for the signal, would you choose to be born?
What's the alternative?

Do you believe in the resurrection of the body?
I have my moments of doubt.

Games

What we need is more Research on Poverty.

A little money would help too.

You scientists better
give some thought to rejoining
the humanistic tradition.

Where do you
find it?

Everything is fine --
now that we have a
tranquilizer in the White House.

I still
feel jumpy.

Our technology is getting out of control.
I've noticed that.

Do you think I should
pour tea for the Russians?

Let them bring
their own samovar

My son must marry a nice Rajput girl.

Some traditions you have to keep.

Gaps

What has suddenly happened to your superego?

Up against the wall!

The future belongs to us.
Are you sure we want it?

Could you apply your conceptual framework to help us to understand the rebellious students?

They love their mothers and hate their fathers-- the dirty little bastards.

Is it possible
to live in absurdity?
I salute your question.

Why are you so old-fashioned?
My roots are in the nineteenth century.

BULLSHIT
In my day we said Point of Order.

As an anarchist-pacifist-vegetarian apostle of non-violence, and member of the Loving Theatre, what is your message for us?

Fuck you.

What are the main impediments to restructuring the university?

The administration, the faculty, and the students.

Why are you so disruptive
in your tactics?

I belong to
the revolutionary mob

At our Center for the Study of Aggressive Behavior, we never speak of violence with a capital V.

That's very sensible of you.

Daddy, why did you make me so rich, and so devoid of ethical convictions?

It seemed a good combination at the time.

Do you believe that genuine communication between people is possible?

I couldn't say.

If God is dead, science is evil, liberals are irrelevant, and Freud is a fink, what is there left to believe in?

The I-Ching

Bombs

Do your studies demonstrate that American society can recover from a nuclear attack?

Yes! all except the people.

We have food that can last for 2,641 1/2 days during post-attack recovery.
I'm not hungry.

What are your scholarly conclusions concerning the biomedical and psychosocial effects of nuclear war?

Ugh.

What is the best preparation for post-attack recovery?

Pre-attack restraint.

We must build more weapons to keep the peace.

Who'll keep the weapons?

Our relationship to nuclear weapons is unhealthy.

Let us not get too abstract.

We might just as well drop the bomb now and get it over with.

Boom

If they build bigger missiles to combat our anti-missiles, then we'll build still bigger anti-missiles, which will require them to build still bigger missiles.

That's terribly reassuring.

Heads

Would you say that mankind has gone mad?
Yes and no.

I'm afraid of the world.
There's something dark about it.

That's just your
imagination, my child.

At times I am very depressed, and at other times exhilarated.
Which are you now?

How do you know that
your patients suffer from
loss of boundaries of the self?

I can never
find them.

On the basis of your careful research study, would you say that it is possible to have an identity?

I could not do more than speculate on that problem.

What would be your psychiatric definition of a rational man?

A guy who agrees with me.

What can psychiatry do for underdeveloped nations?

Not very much.

Prejudices

When an artist puts
a goat on the canvas,
how can you say he is
creating a work of art?

It's the wonderful
question he's asking.

Do you think that putting a real lawn-mower on the canvas makes a better work of art than painting one on?

Depends on how high your grass is.

I loved your book -- except for its misleading argument and failure to reach any conclusions.
It's nice to have admirers.

We can play chess, then checkers, then scrabble, then trouble.

What about after that?

Now that you have won the International Book Award, what do you have to say?

All right -- now we begin our New Year's resolutions.

I pass.

ABOUT THE AUTHOR

Robert Jay Lifton is a research professor of psychiatry at Yale University, and is the author of *Death in Life,* winner of the National Book Award in the Sciences for 1969.